STRESS

AND HOW TO DEAL WITH IT

by

Éilís Bergin PBVM and Eddie Fitzgerald SDB

Dedication

To Marie, Jim and Marja-Liisa
Whose acceptance of adversity and determination
to respond with flexible survival strategies
is a constant source of inspiration to us.

Cover and other Artwork: © Volk

Published and designed by:
SDB MEDIA, St. Teresa's Rd., Dublin 12
Phone: (01) 456 0921   Fax: (01) 455 8781
E-mail: sdbmedia@tinet.ie
WWW: homepage.tinet.ie/~sdbmedia

Distributed by:
Pallas Publications, P.O. Box 50,
Pallaskenry, Co. Limerick, Ireland
Tel: (061) 393 223   Fax: (061) 393 354

Authors Contact:
SDB MEDIA, address, tel, fax, e-mail and WWW above.

LEARNING FROM THE TORTOISE

Many people pick up this booklet because they are intrigued by the cover. That's one of the reasons we chose it. But for us, in addition to being eye-catching, it's also symbolic of an approach to good stress management.

Long ago Aesop told the wonderful story about the tortoise and the hare. The hare was a speed-merchant who was dismissive of the opposition and got side-tracked on his journey. The tortoise wasn't built for speed. Indeed, wherever he went he carried his house on his back. But he was single-minded and had learned the art of making haste slowly. That's why he won the race. He was wise enough to know that:

- If you don't pace yourself, you will simply burn out.
- You will progress nicely by making haste slowly.
- You may lose the sprint, but you can still win the race.
- The ability to be patient is a sure recipe for success.
- Tranquillity of heart isn't found in the fast lane.

BAD NEWS, GOOD NEWS

The bad news is that, no matter what our circumstances, most of us from time to time feel stressed. The pressures of life sometimes get too much for us and we find the load we're carrying almost too heavy to bear. We understand all too well the famous cry: "Stop the world, I want to get off!"

In all probability you have already experienced this in your own life. Maybe right now you're in the middle of the so-called 'rat race', with all the hassle and worries of the workplace, of trying to make ends meet. Perhaps you're unhappy with the way your relationships with family and friends are going. It's possible that you may be carrying the burden of illness, of unemployment, of being the sole carer of a dependent relative. These are all normal causes of stress.

However, the good news we'd like to share with you is that we _can_ stop the world. We can get off the treadmill and take simple preventive steps to counter the most distressing effects of stress on our lives. The rat race is for rats, not for human beings.

This is something that many people have already learned the hard way. When we started writing this booklet we discussed it with some friends of ours. One was a Lloyds Name facing the prospect of losing his entire life savings. The other had been made redundant and was learning to cope with life on the dole. They suggested two things. The first was that we explain clearly what a destructive force stress can be. And the second was that we give some practical, down-to-earth ways to help people take charge of their lives. We have tried our best to do just that.

A SIMPLE 4-STEP PROGRAMME

The various ways in which stress can be alleviated and even, frequently, prevented are quite simple to understand and easy to practise. Indeed, their very simplicity is often the reason why they are not more often put into effect.

The fact that something is obvious, easy or apparently simple does not mean that it should be dismissed as simplistic and of no value. It was Einstein, after all, who said: "Things should be made as simple as possible, but no simpler."

That's precisely what we hope to do in this booklet. We're going to suggest a simple 4-step programme for successful stress management which everybody can make use of. There are no prizes for racing through the steps. There's no finishing tape on the final page. Go at your own pace. Remember the wisdom of the tortoise.

If you do, you're likely to be in for a surprise. The truth is that even the smallest steps can help us reach our goal. It's often the little things which enrich our lives most.

So what's the secret? In a nutshell it's this:

1. Know Yourself:
What kind of person am I? What's my underlying personality type? After all, the more we know about ourselves, the more we will understand what our weaknesses are and consequently what is likely to cause us stress. But, more importantly, we will also begin to appreciate what our individual strengths are and how they can help us deal with whatever pressures come our way.

2. Know Your Enemy:

Unless we know our enemy we cannot possibly begin to deal with it successfully. It's crucial to know what we're up against so that we can begin to develop coping strategies. It's vital to know what stress is, what causes it and what effects it has on our lives. Although most of us choose to ignore it, there's a positive side to stress. Like most enemies, it isn't all bad.

3. Know Your Friends:

Our friends are the various stress skills, techniques and strategies which help us cope with whatever pressures we are experiencing. There are a wide variety of coping mechanisms at our disposal and we will be highlighting some of them. Again, even the simplest technique may well prove to be the key which unlocks the door to freedom and tranquillity in a particular case.

4. Learn To Love All Three:

This final step of learning to befriend our self, our enemy and our friends is vital for any successful stress management. We can learn to tolerate a great deal of what we now consider to be intolerable stress if we learn the core of this message. Love is the wisdom which lightens all loads, and brings with it the gift of peace.

KNOW YOURSELF

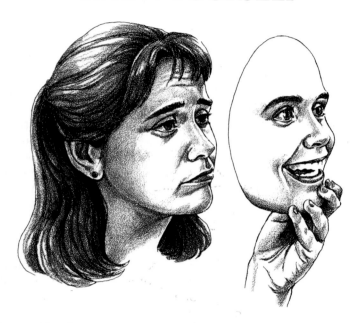

For much of our lives most of us wear a mask. We take on a persona which allows us to put a brave face on things and protect our inner vulnerability. We have a public face and a private one. Sometimes we are so successful that even we ourselves do not know the difference. The face we see in the mirror may cover up more than it reveals. We feel comfortable in our roles as mother, father, doctor, patient, employee, manager, teacher, student or whatever. We've played the part so well and for so long that we can easily mistake what we do for who we are.

In the course of time our mask becomes such a tight fit that it's like a second skin. It scares us even to contemplate taking it off and having a good look at who we really are.

But self-knowledge is essential if we are to grow as human beings. As Socrates pointed out: "The unexamined life is not worth living." Getting in touch with who we are and what makes us tick is imperative if we are ever going to counter the stress in our lives.

One of the principal reasons why we have personal problems is that we don't know who we are and what actually motivates us. Many of us live on a superficial level and are content with that. When we truly begin to know ourselves we learn how to manage our lives better and, in particular, how to improve our relationships with other people.

There's no need to be afraid of this process of digging beneath the surface. It has nothing to do with the morbid navel-gazing which so many people mistakenly believe will give them personal insight. It's just a basic, common sense approach to human psychology.

We're all a mixture of light and shade. We have our good points and our bad. Mature people are aware of how important it is to be able to tell the difference. When we learn to understand and accept ourselves for who we are, we're often surprised to find, as Carl Jung pointed out, that our 'shadow' is 90% gold.

PERSONALITY TYPES

It's not necessary in a booklet on stress management to go into a detailed presentation of personality types. It's enough for our purposes to indicate a couple of approaches which we believe will be helpful when it comes to dealing with stress.

If you want to follow it up at greater depth it would be very helpful to take an extra-mural course on basic psychology, or attend one of the many workshops available on personal development, psychosynthesis, mid-life crisis, Myers-Briggs typology indicator, journaling, dreams or the Enneagram. There are numerous books now available on all of these subjects.

Type A & B Graph

For now, a useful place to start is the distinction between Type A and Type B personalities. We have designed a grid which you can fill in quite easily (cf. page 10). Simply put a dot in the box which most closely approximates to your predominant attitude or behaviour.

For example, if you are always on time and never late, you could place your dot in the box nearest the word 'Punctual'. However, if you don't worry about timekeeping and are genuinely unhurried, put the dot in the box nearest to 'Unhurried'. If you are somewhere in between these extremes, you have a box scale of 1 - 9 to choose from.

Personality Type A & B Grid

Type A									Type B
Punctual	☐	☐	☐	☐	☐	☐	☐	☐	Unhurried
Very Competitive	☐	☐	☐	☐	☐	☐	☐	☐	Non-Competitive
Interrupt	☐	☐	☐	☐	☐	☐	☐	☐	Listen
Restless; Moving	☐	☐	☐	☐	☐	☐	☐	☐	Calm; Still
Hassled	☐	☐	☐	☐	☐	☐	☐	☐	Relaxed
Quick	☐	☐	☐	☐	☐	☐	☐	☐	Slow
Reactive	☐	☐	☐	☐	☐	☐	☐	☐	Responsive
Driven; Uptight	☐	☐	☐	☐	☐	☐	☐	☐	Easy-going
Suspicious	☐	☐	☐	☐	☐	☐	☐	☐	Trusting
High Expectations	☐	☐	☐	☐	☐	☐	☐	☐	Low Expectations
Serious	☐	☐	☐	☐	☐	☐	☐	☐	Playful
Rigid	☐	☐	☐	☐	☐	☐	☐	☐	Flexible
Can't Delegate	☐	☐	☐	☐	☐	☐	☐	☐	Cooperative
Busy; Workaholic	☐	☐	☐	☐	☐	☐	☐	☐	Leisurely
Precise	☐	☐	☐	☐	☐	☐	☐	☐	Vague
Angry	☐	☐	☐	☐	☐	☐	☐	☐	Serene
Insecure	☐	☐	☐	☐	☐	☐	☐	☐	Confident
Anxious	☐	☐	☐	☐	☐	☐	☐	☐	Peaceful
Touchy; Defensive	☐	☐	☐	☐	☐	☐	☐	☐	Accepts Criticism
Unyielding	☐	☐	☐	☐	☐	☐	☐	☐	Compromising
Blames	☐	☐	☐	☐	☐	☐	☐	☐	Praises
Impatient	☐	☐	☐	☐	☐	☐	☐	☐	Patient
Resentful	☐	☐	☐	☐	☐	☐	☐	☐	Forgiving
Animated Speech	☐	☐	☐	☐	☐	☐	☐	☐	Slow Speech
Feelings Repressed	☐	☐	☐	☐	☐	☐	☐	☐	Open Feelings
Personal Deadlines	☐	☐	☐	☐	☐	☐	☐	☐	No Set Deadlines
Ambitious	☐	☐	☐	☐	☐	☐	☐	☐	Satisfied
Short-term view	☐	☐	☐	☐	☐	☐	☐	☐	Long-term view
Detailed	☐	☐	☐	☐	☐	☐	☐	☐	Unsystematic
Egocentric	☐	☐	☐	☐	☐	☐	☐	☐	Unselfish
Many Activities	☐	☐	☐	☐	☐	☐	☐	☐	One At A Time

NOTES:

Place a dot in the box which most closely approximates to your predominant attitude or behaviour (scale of 1 - 9) . When finished, simply join up the dots to make a rough graph. You will then see to what extent you tend to be a Type A (on the left) or Type B personality.

Right at the bottom of the list are the opposites 'Many Activities' and 'One At A Time'. This refers to what is known as polyphasic performance or thinking. For instance, if you find yourself eating your breakfast cereals while feeding the baby, reading the paper, keeping an ear cocked to the news on the radio and answering the phone between mouthfuls, tick the box nearest 'Many Activities' - with whichever hand is free at the time!

When you have completed the list, join the dots to get a rough graph which will give you a good indication as to whether you are a predominantly Type A personality or a Type B. As you will have noticed, Type A behaviour is listed on the left of the grid and Type B on the right. It's worth taking your time filling in the grid. Let the implications of each pair of attitudes or behaviours sink in.

It's important to understand that you are not a better person if you are Type B rather than Type A. You are no better or worse, just different. The fact is that both types can and do experience stress. It's just that their thresholds are different, as are their innate strengths and weaknesses. Fortunately, each type can learn new and valuable coping skills to deal with the stresses they encounter.

Significance of Type A & B
It's worth noting that, according to the available research, people who currently suffer from heart disease are *seven times* more likely to be Type A than Type B personalities. In addition, Type A personalities are more than twice as likely as Type B to get an acute heart attack. It makes sense, therefore, if you find that you are a Type A personality, to learn to modify your behaviour in order to reduce this risk .

Type A personalities also seem to be much more vulnerable to the stresses of modern living. They tend to have a 'short fuse', are easily upset and find it difficult to adapt. They are very competitive, and are so determined to remain in control of their lives that they expend a great deal of mental and physical effort to counter even the apparent threat of losing such control.

Because of this, they are generally unaware of the extent of the tension building up within them and will deny what to others is quite obvious. Their natural style of coping with stress is to be aggressively hyper-responsive. They don't stop till they drop. By then, of course, it is often too late and they end up in a state of collapse.

Type B personalities, on the other hand, are slower to get upset and don't fly off the handle at the least thing. Their placid temperament protects them from the wear-and-tear of life's minor inconveniences. But they can be prone to low-level stress.

There's a wide range of possibilities within any one type from extreme to moderate. It may well be that the healthiest, most resilient and resourceful individuals are somewhere in between the two types, forming a Type AB.

COMPULSIVE MOTIVATIONS

Another major help towards stress management is knowing what actually motivates us. The truth is that many of us are out of touch with who we really are. We have not made the inner journey to find out what drives us, what energizes us, what keeps us going when the chips are down.

For what it's worth, we've found that the theory of personality types known as the Enneagram is a very helpful way of finding out what makes us tick. There are now many books on the subject, including our own, *An Enneagram Guide.*

The Enneagram suggests that human beings essentially fall into one of nine different personality types. We cannot expand on it in this booklet, but it may prove useful just to outline the nine different types and show how they experience stress. Later, when discussing Self-Talk, we will indicate the elements which each type can work on to minimize the stressors in their lives.

For each of the nine personality types (*cf. page 13*), we indicate what their basic motivating compulsion is and how this can lead to their experiencing stress in different ways. It's not possible here to go into each type in detail. Suffice it to say that in addition to experiencing the same kinds of stress that everybody else experiences, each individual personality type is particularly prone to certain kinds of stress because of their own special inner motivation.

Perfectionists
To explain briefly what is meant, let's take the first personality type listed. Perfectionists are people who are very idealistic,

Stress and Personality Types

5. OBSERVER

Analytical, perceptive, reflective and self-contained people. Motivated by their need to know and understand. Stressed when required to share their feelings or get personally involved in projects.

1. PERFECTIONIST

Idealistic, principled, orderly and conscientious people. Motivated by their need to be right. Stressed when they say 'yes' too quickly, don't delegate, and things don't match their unrealistic expectations.

6. SUPPORTER

Loyal, dutiful, hospitable and caring people. Motivated by their need for security and fear of making mistakes. Stressed when uncertain, when in leadership roles and when they see the rules being broken.

2. HELPER

Caring, generous, warm, and attentive people. Motivated by their need to be needed and loved. Stressed by their difficulty in saying 'no', and by having to reveal their own needs and let others to take care of them.

7. OPTIMIST

Fun-loving, gregarious, impulsive and charming people, with many irons in the fire. Motivated by their need to be happy. Stressed when tied down to a single project or forced to confront painful issues.

3. ACHIEVER

Self-confident, adaptable, energetic and outgoing people. Motivated by their need to succeed and be the centre of attention. Stressed at the prospect of failure, loss of status and any threat to their self-image.

8. LEADER

Resourceful, self-confident, energetic and earthy people. Motivated by their need to be in control. Stressed when faced with their own weakness or having to reveal their vulnerable inner child to others.

4. ARTIST

Intuitive, creative, sensitive and expressively warm people. Motivated by their need to be special. Stressed by misunderstanding, by vulgar insensitivity and by conflict in feelings and relationships.

9. MEDIATOR

Calm, laid-back, unpretentious and reassuring people. Motivated by their need to be calm and at peace. Stressed when they have to face difficult issues, meet deadlines or confront others.

principled and conscientious. They have a keen sense of right and wrong and try their best to be scrupulously fair. They are critical of themselves and others for any lapse from the high standards they set. They strive to be methodical and well organized, and they believe that if a thing is worth doing at all, it's worth doing perfectly. They find it very difficult to delegate because they don't trust others to perform tasks properly. Often they think there's only one right way to do things, and that's generally *their* way.

It's very easy to see how this can lead to stress in all sorts of ways. When we don't delegate, we are frequently left with more work to do than we can possibly cope with. When we take everything seriously and concentrate on even the minutest details, is it any wonder that we become stressed when we find things out of place? When we are touchy, critical and judgemental we alienate those who might help us deal with our stressors. We end up being our own worst enemy. For that matter, so do all the other types.

Knowing ourselves, therefore, is the first essential step to successful stress management.

KNOW YOUR ENEMY

We have just seen that the first way to begin to deal with our stress is to get to know ourselves better. That's because the way we see ourselves largely determines what we find stressful and how well we're able to respond to it. The fact is that no two people experience stress in quite the same way.

> *"Two men looked out through prison bars;*
> *one saw mud, and the other saw stars."*

If it's true that what is stressful for one may be an exhilarating experience for another, then a definition of stress is going to be difficult to come up with. But it's vital to try. The more we know about stress, the more we will understand its physical, mental, emotional, behavioural and spiritual effects in our own lives and in the lives of others. Then we can begin to defend ourselves and take preventive measures as soon as we identify the warning signs.

Getting to know our enemy is the second essential step to successful stress management. We need to know what we can about our enemy before we even begin to look for our friends. The fact is that if we don't know our enemy, we won't know which friends to call on for help.

Positive Stress

In this booklet we are going to talk about stress as our enemy, because that's the way most people generally view it. But it's important to remember that even our enemies have their good points. It's vital that we don't get hung up on seeing stress in totally negative terms. There's a positive side to it also.

For example, when we take part in competitive sports, or are involved in a loving and intimate relationship with someone, these activities actually produce a stress response in our bodies. Since such activities are both challenging and stimulating and their outcome is not certain, they get our adrenaline pumping. But we tend to forget the fact that they are stressful because they generally produce such strong positive emotions in us. The enthusiasm, happiness and joy we experience when we are competing in sporting events or involved in a loving relationship usually far outweigh the negative elements of uncertainty, anxiety and jealousy.

Interestingly, when we pick up on these positive energies our resistance to stress is actually increased and our capacity to cope with setbacks grows. This is an insight which, as we will see, can help us deal with the negative stress in our lives.

WHAT IS STRESS?

We all need a challenge in our lives. Without it the spring goes out of our step and our lives become monotonous, unproductive and frustrating. Our creative juices and coping mechanisms work best under a certain amount of pressure. The problem is getting the balance right. If the strings of a violin are too loose they will not play properly, but if they are too tight they will snap.

It's the same with the human body. Too little pressure is as bad as too much. Pressure involves the exertion of continuous force, coercion or restraint on someone or something. Of itself, it is neither positive nor negative. The strings of a violin produce their notes by being stretched to a particular tension.

For human beings there is an optimum level of pressure which each individual can cope with without being overstretched. This varies from person to person. We're all different. What exhausts one will energize another. But, no matter who we are, there comes a point beyond which genuine fatigue leads to exhaustion and burn-out (cf. *Performance Curve on page 17*).

Ability to Cope
A healthy self-image depends in great measure on our ability to deal with life's problems effectively. The central element in all stress is our belief that we are no longer able to cope. The fact that this belief may be mistaken is neither here nor there. The reality is that most people who experience stress *do* have within them the ability to cope with it. The problem is they

PERFORMANCE CURVE

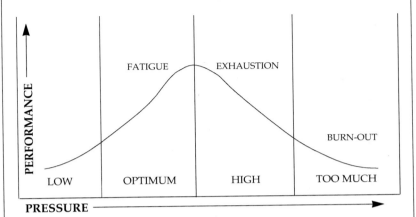

PERFORMANCE (vertical axis)

FATIGUE   EXHAUSTION

BURN-OUT

LOW   OPTIMUM   HIGH   TOO MUCH

PRESSURE ⟶

LOW STIMULATION	BEST STIMULATION	OVER-STIMULATION	DISINTEGRATION
LETHARGY	EFFICIENCY	TENSION	ADDICTION
BOREDOM	ENERGY	DISORGANIZATION	CHRONIC ILLNESS
INDECISION	DECISION	INSOMNIA	DEPRESSION
DISSATISFACTION	FLEXIBILITY	AGGRESSION	BURN-OUT
FRUSTRATION	SELF-CONFIDENCE	INSECURITY	HEART ATTACK
APATHY	ACHIEVEMENT	ILLNESS	DESPAIR
DEPRESSION	CREATIVITY	DISTRESS	SUICIDE

NOTES ON PRESSURE LEVELS

LOW PRESSURE is stressful. It is a particular problem for the unemployed and for those with repetitive and undemanding jobs. Lethargy is destructive and boredom can be soul-destroying. Without the challenge to achieve, we under-utilize our skills and even lose our sense of purpose and meaning in life.

OPTIMUM PRESSURE allows us to live a balanced, integrated life. Our performance is enhanced by manageable pressure and leaves us with a sense of well-being and achievement.

HIGH PRESSURE leads to exhaustion and diminishes our performance. If we go into over-drive rather than heed the warning signals, we only compound our problems and suffer severe anguish and distress.

TOO MUCH PRESSURE over a prolonged period overloads the system, which disintegrates under it. Tragically, the results can be fatal.

don't see it that way. They're so caught up in their stress-induced vicious circle and trapped in negative feelings that they can't even think straight.

So, for what it's worth, here is our definition of stress:

Stress is an unrelieved experience of the pressure of too many demands on an individual, frequently over a lengthy period of time, which evokes a feeling of not being able to cope. In essence, it is the perceived imbalance between our ability to cope and the demands we have to face.

The fact of the matter is that when we think the demands being made upon us have begun to outweigh our resources, we start to experience stress. When our ability to cope is threatened in some way, we begin to see ourselves as a failure. It is vital, therefore, if we are ever going to manage our stress that we learn to develop our coping skills.

Let's now try to find out more about what we perceive to be our 'enemy'. For the moment we'll make the presumption that we all know what stresses us, but as we go on it may well become clear that this isn't entirely so.

OUR PRIMITIVE STRESS RESPONSE

Millions of years ago, when humans first walked the earth, they found that their very survival depended on how they responded to the immediate threat of danger.

Their bodies developed an automatic red-alert response mechanism which we call the fight, fright or flight response. This automatically clicked in when they were confronted with danger. They would instinctively sum up the situation and either fight to protect themselves or their young, freeze in terror like a rabbit under a searchlight, or hightail it out of there as quickly as possible.

When they responded by fighting or running away this helped relieve the automatic build-up of tension in their bodies and eventually their nervous system returned to normal. If they froze and managed to survive, this process would take much longer.

We've all inherited this primitive stress response mechanism. It's built into our genes and automatically switches on when we perceive we're in danger. In a life-threatening situation this can be very important. Anyone who has been chased by a bull will be glad of getting the extra burst of speed.

What normally happens is that, when the immediate danger is over, the para-sympathetic nervous system clicks in to calm us down and return the body to its normal state. If the cause of the stress (stressor) continues, our body's alarm system continues to operate and this can cause temporary or even permanent harm.

Modern Problems

However, the problem is that the stresses of modern life are vastly different from those which faced our original ancestors. For a start, they don't always involve life and death situations. Consequently, the response mechanisms which were originally developed so that human beings could survive are often no longer appropriate. When undischarged, they can actually be damaging.

For example, suppose we are driving a car and another driver pulls in front of us without adequate warning. The first thing that happens is that instantaneously our sympathetic nervous system goes into action. Our body automatically prepares itself for fight or flight. Yet, in the circumstances, we can do neither.

It would be stupid for us to try to regain our place in heavy traffic, and we cannot get out of the car when moving. So we end up either pounding the wheel, or shouting and gesticulating at the offending driver in an attempt to get rid of the stress mechanisms which have built up in our bodies.

Whenever we are faced with major change or having to deal with the unknown, our bodies respond in essentially the same way, no matter whether the issue is largely positive (marriage) or negative (job loss). The various crises we daily experience send our stress levels up. If the stress is unrelieved it will continue to build up until it eventually begins to cause us harm, not just physically, but psychologically and spiritually as well.

It's helpful to look at what actually happens to our body

during stress and to note the damage that can result if our primary stress responses are allowed to go on too long. The physical dangers of living with too much stress add up to a rather depressing list. However, the good news is that we *can* take steps to minimize the risks and shortly we will provide a variety of techniques to help us do just that.

When confronted with a particularly stressful situation our bodily reactions kick in automatically. Here is what happens:

#1. Adrenalin is released into the bloodstream.
This helps speed up physical and mental reflexes, and arouses survival emotions such as anger and fear.
Undischarged, it leaves the person 'uptight', on edge and frustrated, leading to disturbed sleep patterns, impatience and high anxiety.

#2. Cortisone is released.
This helps breathing by shutting off allergic reactions.
Undischarged, it lowers the body's immune system and increases the risk of infection. This means that allergies (like asthma) get worse and minor illnesses (like colds) are harder to get rid of.

#3. Breathing is increased.
This helps increase the oxygen supply to the blood.
Undischarged, it results in sighs, breathlessness, leading to hyperventilation, dizzy spells and fainting (blackouts).

#4. Thyroid hormones are released.
This helps boost the body's metabolism, increasing the rate at which energy is burned.
Undischarged, it can result in weight loss and nervousness, leading to exhaustion and physical collapse.

#5. Sugar and insulin are released into the blood.
This helps give energy to the body as a short-term pick-me-up.
Undischarged, it can cause or aggravate diabetes and lead to hypoglycaemia.

#6. Cholesterol is released.
This helps provide a long-term energy supply from the liver.
Undischarged, it can result in hyperactivity, an inability to relax, leading to irritability, exhaustion and the hardening of the arteries (arteriosclerosis).

#7. Pulse rate is raised.
This helps speed up the supply of oxygen to the muscles.
Undischarged, it results in blood pressure going up, leading to headaches, palpitations and a tendency to heart problems and cardiac arrest.

#8. Digestion shuts down.
This helps the body to divert blood to the brain and the muscles, especially the heart and lungs, giving an increase in energy.
Undischarged, it results in a dry mouth, loss of appetite, gastric juice secretion, 'butterflies' and nausea, leading to indigestion, bad breath, constipation and ulcers.

#9. Muscles are tensed.
This helps the body get ready for strenuous activity. This generally means it becomes rigid, with the fists clenched, the jaws tightened and the shoulders braced for action.
Undischarged, the tension remains in the muscles, causing aches and pains in the neck and shoulders, leading to back pain and spasms.

#10. Mind is alerted.
This helps concentration and the ability to make decisions.
Undischarged, it can keep the mind hyperactive, exhaust its attention span and affect memory, leading to high anxiety and irrational decision-making and behaviour.

#11. Senses are sharpened.
This helps the person take in more information through the five senses, to facilitate taking speedy decisions and action.
Undischarged, it can result in tired eyes (from dilated pupils), intolerance to noise, smells and bright lights, leading to headaches ana social withdrawal.

#12. Skin perspires and hair stands on end.
This sweating helps cool down the body, and regulates temperature during heated exchanges. The 'goose pimples' act as antennae to heighten sensitivity to our surroundings.
Undischarged, the sweating can result in clammy hands and sweaty feet, leading to rashes, acne and eczema; and the tightening of the follicles can lead to hair loss.

#13. Bladder and bowels are emptied.
This helps lighten body weight preparatory to fight or flight.
Undischarged, it results in frequent urination and leads to incontinence

and irritable bowel syndrome.

#14. Emotions are heightened.
This helps to increase motivation to deal with the situation, no matter what the effort.
Undischarged, it results in nervous laughter, tears, shouting and mood swings, leading to aggressive behaviour and violence, or complete withdrawal and depression.

#15. Endorphin is released from hypothalamus.
This helps the body to kill pain. Endorphin is the body's 'feel-good' hormone and is a natural painkiller.
Undischarged, it results in a depletion of endorphin, leaving the body more sensitive than usual to normal aches and pains.

#16. Blood-clotting mechanism is activated.
This helps to stop bleeding by constricting the blood vessels and thickening the blood.
Undischarged, it results in the heart having difficulty pushing the sluggish blood through the veins, leading to thrombosis, heart attack or stroke.

#17. Sex hormone production is reduced.
This helps ensure that energy and attention are not diverted to sexual arousal or concerns related to pregnancy.
Undischarged, it results in decreased libido and other sexual difficulties leading to impotence, frigidity and sterility.

Checklist of Stress Symptoms
We have tried to explain clearly what happens to our bodies when we don't take steps to relieve our stress levels. We haven't done so in an attempt to put the 'frighteners' on. We simply want to highlight how dangerous unrelieved stress really is. It affects us in all sorts of ways, not just physically, but on a mental, behavioural, emotional and spiritual level as well.

It may help to go through the fairly comprehensive checklist (*cf. pages 23-24*) of the various symptoms related to stress. If you find yourself suffering from six or more of these for a month or so, it is likely that you are experiencing unhealthy levels of stress and need to do something about it.

Checklist of Stress Symptoms

The following is a list of the more common effects of chronic stress. It can be used to monitor oneself or others or compile a stress diary. If you are suffering from 6 or more of these symptoms for a month or more, your stress level is unhealthy and you should take remedial action.

PHYSICAL

- Muscle tension
- Spasms
- Backache
- Tension Headaches
- Migraine
- Back Pain
- Aching Neck
- Asthma / Breathlessness
- Clammy Hands
- Sweating
- Cold fingers
- Dry Mouth
- Blood Pressure
- Indigestion
- Peptic Ulcer
- Colds and Coughs
- Sighing
- Hyperventilation
- Clenched Teeth
- Dizziness / Fainting
- Palpitations
- Angina / Chest Pains
- Voice pitch up
- Knotted Stomach
- Twitches
- Shakes (hand, head)
- Tiredness
- Weight Gain

- Anorexia / Weight Loss
- Inarticulate Speech
- Dilated pupils
- Visual Impairment
- Arthritis
- Halitosis
- Constipation
- Irritable Bowel Syndrome
- Diverticulitis
- Piles
- Allergies
- Rashes / Acne
- Eczema
- Hair Loss
- Nausea
- Frequent Urination
- Diarrhoea
- Pacing around
- Restlessness
- Cholesterol Build-up
- Raised Pulse
- Loss of Appetite
- Loss of Libido / Impotence
- High Blood Pressure
- Acute Illness
- Breakdown
- Stroke
- Heart Attack

MENTAL

- Fatigue
- Faulty Memory
- Lack of Concentration
- Indecisiveness
- Lack of Confidence
- Hyper-Arousal

- Impaired Judgements
- Rash Decisions
- Lack of Perspective
- Confused Thinking
- Obsessions
- Breakdown

BEHAVIOURAL

- Slovenliness
- Fastidiousness
- Nail-Biting
- Insomnia
- Over-Sleeping
- Increased Alcohol Intake
- Hair-Pulling
- Increased Smoking
- Erratic or Reckless Driving
- Frowning
- Nervous Laughter
- Reduced Productivity
- Obsessive Behaviours
  (eg. washing, locking up)
- Finger-tapping
- Comfort Eating
- Compulsive Eating
- Hygiene Neglect
- Social Withdrawal
- Non-stop Talk
- Long Breaks / Absenteeism
- Workaholism
- Alcoholism
- Overuse of Stimulants
- Mistakes
- Poor Time-Management
- Accident Prone
- Tardiness / Forgetfulness
- Deadline Failures
- Clock Watching
- Frenetic Activity
- Aggressive Behaviour
- Petty Crime
- Violence
- Major Crime
- Suicide

EMOTIONAL

- Agitation
- Anxiety
- Impatience
- Irritability
- Edginess
- Lower Tolerance Levels
- Over-Exacting
- Worried
- Aggression
- Panic Attacks
- Overreaction
- Inability to Care
- Denial
- Isolation
- Phobias
- Paranoia
- Nightmares
- Insecurity
- Guilt Feelings
- Fearfulness of Criticism
- Hostility
- Outbursts of Anger
- Cynicism
- Mood Swings
- Depression
- Tearfulness
- Exhaustion
- Rage

SPIRITUAL

- Humiliation
- Prayer as Formality
- Attractiveness of Secular
- Priority of Worldly Values
- Strong Temptations
- Weakness / Failures
- Sadness
- Restlessness
- Hopelessness
- Abandonment
- Spiritual Burnout
- Spiritual Desolation

WHAT CAUSES STRESS?

The simple answer is practically anything! It depends on the individual. Weddings, for example, are usually joyous occasions. For some people, however, they bring a great deal of pressure. All the preparations that have to be made can so weigh them down that they are stressed until the whole thing is over. Others breeze through such preparations and even get a 'buzz' out of doing them well. At the opposite end of the scale, funerals are normally sad and traumatic occasions, but with a little help from our friends, most of us manage to cope. Unfortunately, some do not.

There are internal and external, as well as predictable and unpredictable stressors. They come from a wide variety of sources, including work, leisure, finance, family, relationships, religion, accidents, natural disasters, traumatic events, unrealistic goals and expectations, loss of control, and so on.

Holmes Rahe Scale

The well-known *Holmes Rahe Schedule of Recent Life Events* was an attempt to heighten our awareness and encourage us to take preventive measures. It gives a league table of stressors which they found to be likely to lead to our developing a serious illness in the coming year.

These life events range all the way from the death of a spouse, divorce, separation and a jail term, through personal injury or illness, marriage, job loss, retirement, pregnancy and the death of a close friend, to change of work, arguments with a spouse, taking out a mortgage or loan, trouble with in-laws and change of many other kinds (residence, school, social activities, even eating habits).

At the bottom of the list are the stresses associated with holidays or the Christmas season. However, depending on circumstances, the stresses associated with going on holidays or preparing for Christmas could well take on a much more serious aspect in individual cases. The point is that stress is intensely personal.

In the *workplace*, for example, hostile customers, the introduction of new technology, conflicting demands, frequent deadlines, inadequate lighting or ventilation, lack of privacy, a difficult boss, lack of consultation, sexual harassment, office politics and the dreaded threat of redundancy are all likely to produce symptoms of stress over a period of time.

At *home* such things as marital conflict, lack of communication, financial problems, unfaithfulness, snoring, conflicting priorities, jealousy, smoking and drinking habits, debt and moneylenders, a sick or disabled child, truancy, loud music, religious differences, problem teenagers, aging parents, troublesome neighbours, an unplanned pregnancy, and the unrealistic expectations of relatives or in-laws will eventually all take their toll.

All these, and many more, are common causes of stress. Depending on our circumstances, our family and religious background, education, financial situation, state of health, temperament and general approach to life, we may be well able to cope with them, or find that we're so vulnerable that eventually we give way under the sheer weight of the pressure they put upon us.

When our stress is unrelieved, we lock into a vicious circle which compounds our problems and increases our stress levels still further.

Breaking the Vicious Circle
What we hope to do now is to show how we can all take steps to prevent our stress levels building up, and actively to counteract its worst effects. The important thing to realize is that we are not on our own. We do have friends.

KNOW YOUR FRIENDS

Nobody can wave a magic wand and make our stress disappear. We have to be realistic. But the good news is that we *can* develop our resistance to stress and prevent it from dominating our lives.

The rest of this booklet will deal with the essential elements of many different skills. We will also indicate how you can pick-'n-mix from a variety of ingredients to create your own special recipe for successful long-term stress management.

Before dealing with some of the many coping mechanisms at our disposal, we have to repeat that successful stress management begins with getting to know ourselves and getting to know our enemy. Knowing our friends is the *third* step.

Old Friends Are Often Best

There's a lot of wisdom in the old saying, "a friend in need is a friend indeed". When dealing with stress our friends are the various skills, techniques and strategies which help us cope with whatever pressures we are experiencing.

However, if you skipped through the first part of this booklet in order to get to what you think is the 'nitty-gritty', the chances are you'll probably be disappointed. It all looks too simple. Surely there must be a special formula which will do the trick. All the items that follow seem so predictable and uninteresting, apart possibly from aromatherapy massage. It can't possibly be that simple.

The fact is, it can. The difficulty is that it depends greatly on whether you have grasped the implications of what we said in the earlier pages. If, for example, you haven't taken in what we said about stress actually changing our breathing patterns, you'll probably think the whole business of deep breathing is 'for the birds'.

It's interesting how often in life we undervalue the importance of the friends we've grown up with, in our search for new and more exotic ones who will supposedly revitalize our lives and give them a quick fix.

We shouldn't be too quick to dismiss any friend in our time of need. The good news is that *all of these coping mechanisms really do work*. Appearances can be deceptive. The suggestions

27

which follow have been tried by people from all walks of life and have been found to be very successful.

DEEP BREATHING

We begin and end our life with a breath. Every day of our lives in between we take up to 20,000 breaths, most of which we are unaware of. We take in about a litre a minute. Breath is life. But it is also spirit. Indeed, the word *spiritus* in Latin is used for both breath and spirit. The Old Testament talks about God breathing life into human beings.

We need to breathe in order to get oxygen into our system and to expel carbon dioxide. Without oxygen we cannot obtain or burn off the energy we need to live.

The problem is that since breathing is largely automatic, few of us pay attention to it. We don't even realize that deep breathing is a skill. We had it as young children but as we began to grow we learned other ways of breathing for other purposes. As adults we are now content to breathe as we have always done and fail to grasp that some kinds of breathing are inappropriate in certain circumstances.

Deep breathing is perhaps the single most effective way to lower our physical stress levels. Unfortunately, most of us do not practise it. As we saw earlier, one of the first things that happens to us when we are stressed is that our breathing becomes shallow, we begin to take quick breaths and may even end up hyperventilating.

Here is a simple exercise. Place your left hand flat on your chest and your right hand flat on your stomach. Now take a deep breath and hold it for three seconds. Then let it out.

Easy wasn't it? Let's repeat the exercise, but this time observe what happens. Does your chest expand and your left hand rise with it? Or does your stomach expand into a rounded belly and your right hand move with it?

Abdominal Breathing
Normal breathing is from the chest; deep breathing is from the abdomen. When we breathe from the abdomen (like a dog stretched out in front of the fire or a baby asleep in a cot) we breathe deeply and rhythmically, getting rid of toxins and facilitating the transport of nutrients to the bloodstream.

It is worth practising abdominal breathing and getting into the habit of using it from time to time during the day. Sit up straight or lie on your back. Place your hands gently on your abdomen. Relax. Inhale from the pit of your stomach and, as you do so, allow it to expand as fully as possible until you feel yourself becoming pot-bellied. Exhale slowly and gently pull in your stomach muscles.

Repeat the whole exercise for a few minutes. You'll be surprised at how calm and relaxed you'll become in a short time.

It is important to exhale slowly. The trouble is that many people have developed the habit of breathing in for twice as long as they breathe out. Ideally we should breathe out twice as slowly as we breathe in.

When you're not used to doing it, abdominal breathing can seem exaggerated and unnatural. Don't be fooled. It's the most natural thing in the world. Just look at how a baby's tummy rises and falls during sleep. With practise you will find that it gradually becomes easier to do, so that eventually it becomes second nature to you, and you can switch from chest to abdominal breathing at will.

EXERCISE

One of the reasons why many people succumb to various different stressors is that they forget to take proper physical exercise. The old Latin tag 'Mens sana in corpore sano' (a healthy mind in a healthy body), incorporates a great deal of wisdom.

Regular exercise helps keep our cardiovascular and respiratory systems in good condition and makes us feel good by relieving body tensions, restoring our depleted reserves of energy, and releasing endorphin (the 'feel-good' hormone) into our system.

We can all benefit from adopting a healthier lifestyle. However, whatever activity we choose should be enjoyable, otherwise we are unlikely to keep it up. Swimming, athletics, basketball etc. may well be options for some, but all should be able to manage *brisk* walking.

Even if you dislike walking you can always find a way to make it enjoyable. Try listening to your favourite music on a portable cassette recorder as you walk.

NUTRITION

A balanced diet is vital if we are serious about tackling stress. There is no need to take this to extremes. If we do, it will only become another source of stress in our lives. But too many of us regularly eat the wrong foods. This is nowhere more evident than when we feel the need of a 'pick-me-up'. The quick cup of coffee for relief when we are under stress is only going to compound our problems. Here are a few pointers to help you make more informed choices.

☐ *A Balanced Diet*

When we're under stress we consume more carbohydrates, fat and protein. This means that our stores of the B vitamins and vitamin C are depleted and need replenishing. It is important to eat a balanced diet for proper nourishment. Consult your doctor or nutritionist for advice about vitamin supplements.

☐ *Coffee and Tea*

Coffee is a stimulant and releases adrenaline into the body. It perks us up. But when we are under stress our body already produces increased levels of adrenalin, so coffee only adds to our problems. Far from relaxing us, it makes us jumpy (human percolators!), irritable and leads to headaches. If you like the taste of coffee switch to decaffeinated. There is also caffeine in tea, so it is better to use herbal teas or to drink it light.

☐ *Water*

Water intake is important to avoid stress. Between 6 - 8 glasses a day will help to thin the blood, prevent urinary tract problems (infections, stones) and aid digestion.

☐ *Fibre*

It is important to get enough fibre (roughage) in your diet. This is found in plant materials but not in meat or animal products. Vegetables (peas, beans, corn etc.) and fruits are helpful here.

☐ *Fat*

We need fat to store energy, so it is important to have some fat in our diet. However, in general people eat more fat than they really need, so the advice is cut your intake and mix animal and vegetable fats.

☐ *Protein*

Protein is essential for growth. It helps provide us with anti-bodies. However, if we take an excess of protein it just turns to fat or is excreted as nitrogen waste.

☐ *Sugar*

Sugar provides calories without providing either protein, vitamins or minerals. It gives us a short-term energy boost, but it can also lead to a variety of problems from tooth decay and mood swings to malnutrition. Avoid artificially sweetened soft drinks. Take whole fruits instead. Don't use sugar in your tea or coffee and as far as possible stay away from biscuits, cakes and puddings. However, don't go overboard. Don't hesitate to treat yourself occasionally.

☐ *Salt*

Our bodies need salt, but unless we perspire a lot through living in a desert or doing very heavy workouts, we do not need to add salt to our normal diet. Today salt is added to many processed foods and so people eat about twice as much salt as they need. When stressed our blood pressure rises. We don't need salt to push it even higher. Besides, we can always find alternatives to give food a lift - lemon, herbs and spices all do nicely. It is also possible to adapt to the more natural taste of food without salt.

☐ *Alcohol*

Alcohol is another stimulant. It releases stress hormones (eg. hydrocortisone) into the body. Contrary to popular belief, it stimulates the brain and leads to disturbed sleep. It's side effects outweigh its benefits and it is best to do without or at least to cut down drastically on intake. Besides, alcohol is only a temporary escape from our problems. It may numb the pain for a while, but when we return to reality, our problems are still there.

☐ *Eat Slowly and in Moderation*

A simple but effective tip for good nutrition is to eat slowly. This way you will actually taste the food as well as enjoy it. Always eat in moderation and try to avoid the empty calorie foods. This will ensure that you will maintain your optimum weight.

☐ *Learn to live with less*

A principle we have found very helpful is this: if you can't live without it, try your best to live with less.

TIME MANAGEMENT

Time is not our enemy. It is a gift. We live in it as we do in space, air, and light. It is part and parcel of our very being and as such needs to be befriended. When we are happy it *flies*, when we are uninterested it *drags*. We can *kill* it, *spend* it, *fix* it, *do* it, *serve* it, *clock* it, *keep* it, *share* it, look forward to it or look back on it. In fact many of us will do everything with it, except live it fully in the here and now. Stressed people have learned either to abuse it or allow themselves to be abused by it.

The *symptoms* of bad time management are:

Shortage: We never seem to have enough time to relax.
Haste: We're regularly rushing in order to catch up.
Indecisiveness: We're unable to make clear decisions.
Tardiness: We miss deadlines and are rarely on time.
Fatigue: We're chronically tired and feeling drained.
Anxiety: We're overwhelmed by tasks and details.

If we are experiencing any of these symptoms, it makes sense to take steps to sort them out.

Time Diary
The first thing we need to do is find out exactly how we spend our time. It's a great help to take a three-day period and record

everything we do as well as the time it takes (eg. shopping - 30 minutes; driving the car - 40 minutes).

Starting from early morning, this will include getting dressed, eating, travelling, working, shopping, housework, socializing, daydreaming, cooking, looking after the children, reading, watching television, praying, sleeping and so on.

By keeping a record of our various activities and the time we spend on them, we can then get a more accurate picture of where our priorities are right now. We may well be in for a few surprises!

The great thing is that although these are our priorities right now, they don't have to be our priorities in the future. We can always take the necessary steps to take charge of our choice.

If, for example, we are interested in time management in relation to our work, we would naturally make one set of choices. These could include limiting phone conversations, learning to say 'no', and developing the habit of praising people for work well done.

If, on the other hand, we want to use time management to get our lives into some kind of balance, we will need another set of choices. We may well find that, without realizing it, our lives have got out of kilter and that we are spending an inordinate amount of time on areas which do not fully deserve it.

Practical Hints
Whatever our reasons for wanting to manage our time properly, it will help us greatly if we put some or all of the following suggestions into practice. There is no need to try to do everything at once. Take things a step at a time. For a start, you could choose one of these practical suggestions and work on it for a week.

1. *Don't be afraid to delegate work.*
2. *Learn to reward yourself and take adequate recreation.*
3. *Allow sufficient time for tasks to be completed.*
4. *List what needs doing and give priority to the essentials.*
5. *Plan ahead, but allow room for flexibility.*
6. *Finish what you started - see it through to the end.*
7. *Be realistic and build in time for the unexpected.*
8. *Ask for help whenever you need it.*
9. *Learn to pace yourself (remember the tortoise).*

MEDITATION

Some people just turn off at the mere use of the word 'meditation'. It conjures up images of monks and nuns sitting in church for hours on end in silent contemplation. Fine for them, but not for us!

This, of course, is nonsense. It's a caricature of what meditation is about. The fact is that everybody can meditate, not just monks and nuns, and it doesn't have to take hours. When you come right down to it, it's no big deal. But it *is* a big help in stress management.

Life today is lived at a frenetic pace. There's constant noise all around us. We are so busy that we rarely have time to be quiet. Yet without deep inner stillness we cannot hope to combat stress effectively on a long-term basis.

Meditation is one of the best ways we know of for developing what we call 'soul-balance' or harmony of body, mind and spirit. Whenever we are stressed there is an imbalance in our lives which needs to be addressed. Meditation (secular or religious) can help us transcend our compulsiveness and introduce us to forms of deep relaxation which we did not think possible.

When we calm our mind we also help calm our body. During our normal day-to-day activities our brain produces beta waves (at between 14 - 50 cycles a second). When we meditate or use our imagination to visualize a calming scene, we enter into a relaxed state of awareness and our brain begins producing the more calming alpha waves (8 - 13 cycles a second).

Regular practice is the key. If you meditate for just 20 minutes a day you will soon develop a greater inner assurance and a serenity which will give you the courage to deal with whatever challenges the day might bring.

There are many ways of meditating and books abound on the subject. As Christians ourselves, we find Christian meditation very helpful. Authors like William Johnson, John Main and Tony deMello are very helpful. However, whatever form of meditation you adopt, the basic steps are very easy.

A Simple Method
1. Find a warm quiet spot where you will be undisturbed for about 20 minutes.
2. Close your eyes and let your breathing become rhythmic

and deep.

3. Let go of all tension in your body and be aware of how relaxed and calm you are becoming.

4. As you continue to breathe deeply through your abdomen, gently tell yourself that you are calm, at peace and content. If you are doing Christian meditation you can concentrate on a suitable mantra or scriptural text (eg. "I am with you", "Jesus is Lord", "Shalom", "Mar-an-a-tha"), and remain open to hearing God's word. Alternatively, you can visualize yourself in a scene from the scriptures and let God speak to you through it.

5. If your mind wanders, don't get upset. Gently return your attention to your mantra, your scene, your scripture text or whatever you have chosen for your meditation. If you fall asleep, don't fret when you wake up. It will probably have refreshed you!

6. At the end of 20 minutes (which can be timed with a watch alarm or with a tape of appropriate music), gently wriggle your fingers and toes, open your eyes and return to your present surroundings relaxed and renewed.

POSITIVE SELF TALK

Much of what happens in our bodies is totally automatic. We don't, for example, have to think about our breathing, our temperature, our heart rate, which hormones to secrete and other such essential functions. They happen without our being aware of them.

A lot of people do not fully grasp the fact that a significant amount of our thoughts and feelings also operate on a subconscious level. For instance, everyone experiences 'downers' from time to time. These are the negative thoughts and feelings which seem to come to the fore without our knowing precisely why. On examination, they often turn out to be variations on a parental theme, sometimes many years removed. The negative messages we picked up as children are recycled in our day-to-day expectations, beliefs, evaluations and predictions.

For example, we may exaggerate our mistakes or compare ourselves unfavourably with someone successful. "That was stupid. You'll never learn," we say to ourselves. "How can you be so clumsy; Mary did it, but *you* just don't have the knack." Or we may repeat what we were told so often so long ago: "You've never been mechanically minded - you're only wasting your time."

Such negative thoughts inevitably lead to negative feelings and in double-quick time a vicious circle is established. Our self-image is dinted and we become vulnerable to self-fulfilling prophecies.

Stop the Tape

As soon as we find ourselves locked into such negative self-talk it's essential to tell ourselves: "Stop the Tape!" or "Cancel, Cancel!" Then we need to re-programme ourselves with positive attitudes.

There is a perverse kind of security in believing the worst about ourselves. It gives us the excuse not to extend ourselves when tackling the challenges we have to face in life, because we've already convinced ourselves we're losers before we even begin. The end result is that we will begin to live *down* to our expectations.

Each of the nine personality types we mentioned earlier is susceptible to specific ways of running themselves down. To help them (*cf. pages 37-38*) we give some positive 'Coping Cues' appropriate to each individual type. These are specially chosen to reinforce the positive attitudes which each personality type needs to develop. It is not possible in a short booklet to go into the implications of these. Suffice it to say that each statement can be unpacked to provide us with strong positive affirmations, to boost our self-esteem and so lower our vulnerability to negative self-talk.

REFRAMING

This is a very simple technique which helps reduce stress by offering us fresh ways of looking at things. It's a form of lateral or 'upside-down' thinking in our search for positive alternatives. It frequently involves placing events in contexts different from those we originally associated with them. This is because the meaning or significance of an event depends very much on

Coping Cues for Personality Types

1. PERFECTIONIST
- ❏ Lower your ceiling.
- ❏ When you can't cope, simplify!
- ❏ Relax and enjoy the moment.
- ❏ God writes straight with crooked lines.
- ❏ *Forgive and you will be forgiven (Lk 6:37).*

2. HELPER
- ❏ I am loved for myself, not for my service.
- ❏ I need to take care of myself first.
- ❏ I have a right to say 'No'.
- ❏ Love lets go; possessiveness clings on.
- ❏ *Love your neighbour as yourself (Mk 12:31).*

3. ACHIEVER
- ❏ Don't just 'do' something, stand there!
- ❏ I am responsible for what I tame.
- ❏ Dim the headlights and listen to your feelings.
- ❏ I'm loved for myself, not for what I do.
- ❏ *Be still and know that I am God (Ps. 46:10)*

4. ARTIST
- ❏ Bloom where you are planted.
- ❏ The extraordinary lies in the ordinary.
- ❏ The mess is part of reality.
- ❏ I am not my feelings; I can control them.
- ❏ *Think of the flowers (Lk 12:27).*

5. OBSERVER

- ❏ What goes around, comes around.
- ❏ The head doesn't have all the answers.
- ❏ Roll up your sleeves and get stuck in!
- ❏ I have feelings too.
- ❏ *The Word became flesh and dwelt among us (Jn 1:14).*

6. SUPPORTER

- ❏ Toot your own horn!
- ❏ Since I am loved, there's no reason to fear.
- ❏ Light a candle rather than curse the darkness.
- ❏ My authority comes from within.
- ❏ *I am with you, always (Mt 28:20).*

7. OPTIMIST

- ❏ No seed ever sees the flower.
- ❏ Settle down and centre yourself.
- ❏ Happiness is an inside job.
- ❏ Less is more.
- ❏ *Your sorrow will turn to joy (Jn 16:20).*

8. LEADER

- ❏ A problem shared is a problem halved.
- ❏ Get in touch with your tender feelings.
- ❏ Others have feelings too.
- ❏ Risk showing your vulnerability.
- ❏ *Here I am as one who serves (Lk 22:27).*

9. MEDIATOR

- ❏ Face the problems - they won't go away.
- ❏ I am a healer with needs of my own.
- ❏ Every journey begins with the first step.
- ❏ I, too, am worthwhile and much loved.
- ❏ *Every hair on your head is counted (Lk 12:7).*

its context.

For example, suppose you go to a hospital and wait in a queue for fifty minutes for a blood test. Eventually, when you get inside, you find that you've brought the wrong documentation with you (this happened to one of us recently). In such circumstances it's very easy to get stressed by your silly mistake and think the roof has fallen in.

However, by reframing, you can look at it differently. The past fifty minutes were profitably spent reading about thirty pages of a book. Besides, a quick phone-call to your doctor gives the nurse the all-clear to continue with the test. In addition, you realize the whole episode has been a useful learning experience and has reminded you once again of the need to allow yourself adequate time to prepare properly for a variety of different appointments.

There's always another way of looking at things. And, in terms of stress management, it can make all the difference.

IRRATIONAL BELIEFS

Many of us get stressed because we hold on to unreasonable beliefs about life and living, eg. "I must never make a mistake." It's important to find out what irrational beliefs we hold, if we are ever going to replace them with rational alternatives, eg. "It's ok to make mistakes. That's how we learn." Naming our beliefs is a first step to dealing with them. It's impossible to itemize them all, but perhaps some of the following may well ring a bell:

☐ Anything worth doing is worth doing perfectly.
☐ If I don't look after this person, nobody else will.
☐ Others only value me if I am able to produce the goods.
☐ Nobody will ever understand what makes me tick.
☐ It's better to avoid feelings; they only mess you up.
☐ Loyalty means you should never, ever, leave a sinking ship.
☐ Instant gratification is the secret of a happy life.
☐ Adults are not fragile; they can stand up for themselves.
☐ If I put it off long enough, it will eventually go away.

IMAGINATION

Our minds are incredibly creative and resourceful. We can create vivid pictures of absent objects and respond to them as if they were really present. If we imaginatively light a log fire, we will soon begin to smell the smoke; if we bite into a bitter lemon, our mouth will produce saliva automatically.

The fact is that we respond physically and psychologically to the images we create or keep in our mind. This is why we talk about the power of mind over matter, or the 'placebo effect'. It is also the reason why visual imagery is now seen as such a powerful tool for healing people.

The good news is that we can use this image-making ability of ours to help manage our moods, redirect our thoughts, relax our muscles and refresh our spirits. In doing so we can prevent or reduce our stress. Here are two simple 5-10 minute exercises which have proved to be very effective.

Creative Power Nap
Today we understand a great deal more about the body's natural rhythms, and how important it is for us to respect them. For example, by taking a 20-30 minute nap in the early afternoon we can help our body restore lost energy and give it the boost it needs to continue operating at maximum efficiency for

the rest of the day.

But we can also choose to take a 5-minute creative 'power nap' at any stage during a busy day and be assured that it will renew and refresh us. The process is simple and is a mixture of visual imagination and self-hypnosis.

First of all, find a place where you can be undisturbed for 5 or 10 minutes. Sit upright, relaxed not rigid. Rest your hands gently, palms up and open, on your lap. Now, close your eyes and imagine that the place where you are right now is on the tenth floor of your personal building. For the next five minutes you are going to leave that area and all that is happening around you, and go to a place of total peace and tranquillity. It may be your favourite beach, lake, meadow or mountain. You can choose wherever you like best.

In your head, move out of the hustle and bustle of where you are right now and go into your private lift. Close the doors and press the button for the ground floor. The lift begins to move, and as it does, you count slowly as you go down:

9 *You are leaving the day's activity and hassle behind.*

8 *You hear the sounds getting fainter as you slowly go down.*

7 *Already you are relaxing, looking forward to the break.*

6 *Your muscles relax and your stomach unknots.*

5 *You breathe in warmth, and breathe out your worries.*

4 *Your jaw loosens and your shoulders sag. It's so relaxing.*

3 *You feel very calm, as you move closer to your still centre.*

2 *Your breathing is deep and your body completely at rest.*

1 *You are at peace as you go down to your special place.*

The lift stops. The doors open. You walk into your special place. Look around you. Take in the scene. Notice the colour, the shapes, the warmth, the peaceful atmosphere. Make yourself comfortable. You can walk, sit or lie down as you wish. Bask in the warmth and comfort of it all. Breathe in the soothing fragrance of the place. Be still....be present....just *be*.

Rest for a while in this deep inner peace. Give thanks for this place, this still centre. And, knowing that you can return to it at any time, choose now to take with you the memory and feeling and experience of its gentle calm. Move slowly towards the lift. As the doors close behind you, count your journey back, staying with the scene and bringing its peace and deep relaxation with you as you go back up.

When you reach 10 the doors open and you are once again back where you started. Rest for a moment on your chair, then, in your own time, wriggle your toes and fingers, open your eyes and gently come back into the present, totally refreshed and energized. Without rush or hassle, you go about your business once more.

Venetian Blind
Find a warm comfortable spot where you will be undisturbed. Lie down and close your eyes. Relax your body and let your arms rest by your side, palms open and resting on the floor. Scan your body for tension and let go of what you can.

Imagine now that your body is a venetian blind. Starting at your toes and slowly working your way up, begin to roll up the entire length of your body, until you have effectively vanished by the time it reaches the top of your head. Relax for a few moments. Then gently unroll your body from the top of your head, back down to your toes. Rest. Wriggle your toes and fingers as you open your eyes. Get up slowly and feel totally relaxed and refreshed.

AUTOGENIC TRAINING

This relaxation technique is based on the repetition of a series of simple phrases and has proved to be very effective in getting the body's autonomic system to produce the desired physiological responses. Autogenic means self-produced. The technique can be used to:

Develop deep breathing: "My breathing is deep and regular."
Regularize the heart: "My heartbeat is calm and measured."
Relax tense muscles: "My neck muscles are relaxed."
Warm cold limbs: "My right (left) foot (arm etc.) is warm."
Relax the whole body: "My whole body is calm and rested."

It may take a while to get a response when you first begin. But do give the technique a reasonable chance to work before dismissing it. Also, feel free to use whatever positive form of words suits you best.

TENSE AND RELEASE

One simple way to experience what stressed muscles feel like is to do a 'tense and release' exercise with various groups of muscles. The more aware you are of your tension, the more you can do to control it. You can do this with the forehead; eyes; lips; jaw; arms; chest, back and shoulders; abdomen; pelvis; and legs. Briefly, the technique is:

1. Tense the muscle as you breathe in
   (eg. open mouth a swide as you can).
2. Hold the breath and tension for five seconds.
3. Let go of the tension quickly as you exhale.
4. Relax for 20 seconds.

Don't tense too hard or you'll get cramp. If you are already very tense you'll have to tense harder to notice your tension. *Please note that this exercise should not be attempted by people with high blood pressure.*

SPIRITUAL RESOURCES

We human beings are complex creatures. We are body-spirit beings, and these interpenetrate each other. There is no part of us that is just body only. Everything that affects the body in some way also affects the spirit. Interestingly, *everything that affects the spirit, also affects the body.* If I'm troubled in the spiritual dimension of my life, this will somehow or other manifest itself in the physical.

A simple example of this is the man who went to his doctor suffering from stomach ulcer. No treatment was effective until he spoke with a counsellor and talked about how guilty he felt at betraying his wife, by having an affair with a friend. When eventually he sorted out this relationship and received forgiveness, his ulcer responded to treatment.

Regardless of whether we go to church or not, we've all got a spirituality. In simple terms, our spirituality is nothing more than our attempt to live out our lives according to what we believe in. What matters most to us in the long run is what really keeps us going, day in day out. Many so-called religious people may be surprised to find that money or power, not the love of God, is their real bottom-line.

To be whole human beings we need to integrate the physical, spiritual, psychological and emotional elements of our make-up. For successful stress management it is vital to tap into all the spiritual resources we have at our disposal.

LETTING GO

The virtue of letting go is vital for successful stress management. It enables us to tell which values are worth fighting for and which are not. There's no point in wasting energy on trivial issues. It's possible to lose a battle and yet to win a war.

In religious terms the virtue of letting go manifests itself in three main ways: forgiveness, detachment and trust.

Forgiveness

If we have lived at all we have probably learned that whenever we hold on to a grievance, the only one who really suffers is ourselves. We're often our own worst enemy. All too often we cut our nose off to spite our face, and rarely learn the bitter lesson of hoarding resentment. That's why we frequently bring on ourselves many of the damaging effects of stress.

When we're angry at others we raise the stress-producing hormones in our body and misdirect the energy we need to get on with the more positive aspects of our lives. Is it any wonder that we feel drained? We've enough burdens to carry without adding to them.

However, forgiving others is only half the story. We also have to learn to forgive ourselves. Many past mistakes are not really our fault. We are not totally responsible for everything that happens in our lives. If we are ever going to heal the wounds of the past, we must learn acceptance and letting go.

Detachment

Many of us get terribly stressed because our centre is not secure. We get knotted up when our carefully constructed self-image is threatened in any way. We are so hung up on prestige, position, status and power that we go into a flat spin when they are questioned or in danger.

When our centre is secure, we don't have to worry about defending our circumference. When we know that we are truly loved, we can let go of worry. The knowledge of being loved somehow grounds us and gives us an untroubled serenity about our centre, our deepest self. It gives us the capacity to overlook slights and let go of our defensive posturing. It enables us to adopt a gentler, more detached approach to our own self-importance. It liberates us from the negativity of mixed feelings, so that finally we learn how to truly laugh *at* ourselves and *with* others.

Trust
As we learn to trust at depth we begin to let go more and more. This is what the saints called 'holy abandonment'. They were like children who are prepared to jump into the unknown, confident that they will be caught in their father's outstretched arms.

There may well be times in our lives when our confidence in God's love will be our best support and deepest resource. We can learn to grow in trust by taking a favourite scripture quote (*eg. Psalm 34:18 "The Lord is close to the broken-hearted"*) and reminding ourselves of it frequently during the day.

PRAYER

Prayer is our acknowledgement that there is a power greater than ourselves. Christians believe that this ultimate power is God, who loves us unconditionally. Putting our trust in God can be a powerful help in times of stress. Tapping into this peace and serenity is a stress-management resource without parallel. If our relationship with God is weak it's worth remembering that God still loves us and waits patiently for us to rediscover our true selves and the divine presence within.

There are many life-experiences which can cause us to be wary of or reject all hope and trust and love. *The good news is that the hole in our soul can be healed.* The simple fact of being present and attentive to the gaze of Unlimited Love in prayer can and does effect the most amazing transformations.

STRESS RECIPES

Depending on your personality, you can pick-'n-mix from the techniques, skills and tips in this booklet to make up your own personal stress management recipe. To show you what a balanced recipe might look like, we give a sample (*cf. page 46*) for the type we call 'Helpers'. Carers will identify with this type.

SAMPLE STRESS RECIPE FOR HELPERS

BODY: *Share and Stare.*
Your natural bias is to look after other people's needs and to neglect your own. You prefer to minister to others rather than allow them to minister to you. If someone offers to share your work-load, allow them to do so. If nobody offers to help don't be ashamed to ask. Build a half-hour into your daily routine to put your feet up and relax with a tape or good book. Don't allow yourself to be side-tracked by service during that time.

HEART: *Reveal your own concerns.*
Just as it is important to share your physical burdens, it is vital to your emotional health that you share how you feel. Friendship is a two-way relationship. It involves give and take. As a helper type you generally prefer to listen to other people's stories rather than communicate your own. Try telling a friend how you really feel, what your worries are, and what concerns you right now. That way someone else can minister to *you* for a change.

MIND: *Learn to say 'No'.*
Running to other people's assistance every time they call for help does a double disservice. First of all, it prevents others from developing their own coping skills and from learning how to look after their needs. Secondly, their dependence on you makes you dependent on them, feeding into your compulsion to look after them. If you cannot say 'No' to legitimate requests, you cannot truly say 'Yes' when it matters.

SPIRIT: *Sit and listen to God loving you.*
Your natural inclination is to 'do' rather than to *be*. But you *are* a good person. You don't have to prove it all the time by doing. Being who you are is enough. Overextending yourself is an attempt to escape from what you fear might be inner emptiness. But all it leads to is exhaustion and eventual burn-out. A good scripture passage to meditate on, gently and with no self-recrimination, is the story of Martha and Mary (*cf. Lk. 10: 38-42*).

PRACTICAL TIP
Encourage others to do things for themselves. If necessary, show them how, but then leave them to it!

SOME PRACTICAL STRESSBUSTERS

These skills and techniques may appear obvious and commonplace, but they can help us overcome many of the daily hassles which upset us.

1. HUMOUR

Rigidity in thinking and in acting is a prime source of stress. Laughter is frequently a better medicine than tranquillisers or mood-enhancing drugs. It releases hormones which alleviate pain. Special 'laughter clinics' have been opened in the USA where they show comedy films. Humour uncorks the pressure and releases tension for many people. It allows them to gain perspective on their problems and to lighten up. The importance of the clown was well known in the middle ages, when every king employed a court jester to prevent him from taking himself too seriously.

2. REWARDS

Wise parents know that whenever they have to encourage their children to face a painful situation there is nothing like a reward to provide an incentive. Using the same principle, whenever you are faced with a difficult challenge, plan to give yourself a treat afterwards. The possibilities are many: a meal with a friend, a new item of clothing, a relaxing bath, a few hours listening to your favourite music. You'll find that this simple technique of having something to look forward to will help you cope much better. It will motivate you to perform the task and so make a positive contribution to your morale and self-esteem. Don't hesitate to pamper yourself after a stressful day.

3. STABILITY ZONES

In the Peanuts cartoon strip, Linus had his security blanket. Many children naturally find their own comfort corner. Adults do well to recognize that it is important in our busy world to have a safe haven from all the pressures which beset us. A stability zone is something we can hold on to, someone we can rely on, someplace we can go to in order to find a sense of balance and tranquillity. It can be a *person* (aunt, friend, colleague), *place* (meadow, beach, jacuzzi) or *routine ritual* (a long bath, a country walk, fishing). It is where we find support, strength, inner peace, and personal affirmation. No matter what happens we always know what to expect and where we stand.

4. NATURE

Taking in the beauty of nature has a wonderfully calming effect on people. A walk in the mountains, a ramble in the woods, or a stroll along the beach can refresh the tired spirit and creatively distance you from your immediate troubles. Taking time to smell the flowers, to feel the texture of the bark of a tree, or to observe the detail of a spider's web helps locate us in the wider scheme of things and relativize our problems.

5. MASSAGE

Human touch is vital for our personal growth and development. Massage is a special form of therapeutic touch which kneads tense muscles and stretches them out again, thus easing the various aches and pains associated with them. It helps relax the body and so relieve tiredness.

There are a wide variety of massage techniques available today, among them reflexology and aromatherapy. It is well worth learning how to massage. Find someone you trust with whom you can share this healing technique or go to a qualified person when you are feeling stressed.

6. AROMATHERAPY

Fragrance has always had a powerful effect on people. Aromatherapy is a form of healing which uses essential oils obtained from flowers, plants, trees and leaves. They are then diluted and mixed in various proportions depending on their properties and the needs of the individual.

Aromatherapy can help ease tension, headache and depression. It also tones and relaxes tired muscles. The oils can be used in burners, in the bath, as a compress or in massage. It's worth going to a qualified aromatherapist since some oils irritate the skin and can even be harmful under certain conditions.

7. REFLEXOLOGY

Reflexology is a very relaxing

massage which applies pressure to the feet or hands. According to the theory behind this quite ancient therapy, the reflex points located in both feet and hands correspond to the ten energy zones that are to be found running the length of the body. They are, as it were, a map of the body's energy flow and so the reflexologist, by working on the feet or hands, is actually treating the corresponding parts of the body. The technique is both safe and non-invasive. It stimulates the circulation and cleanses the body of various toxins. At the same time it induces deep relaxation and so contributes to stress reduction.

8. WORRY BOX

Many people are 'worriers'. They waste much valuable time turning things over in their mind, like a dog at a bone. Frequently they can't get to sleep because their mind is still in its anxious mode.

A very effective way to stop this needless fretting is to make a worry box, and have a set half-hour period each day for worrying about things. Simply jot down what is worrying you and then give yourself permission to put it aside until your pre-set 'worry period' comes round. Or just say to yourself, "I'll worry about that at 9.30 tomorrow morning. I won't let it bother me now." Inevitably, many things which harassed us yesterday will have sorted themselves out by the time our 'worry period' comes round!

9. GET IT OUT!

It is vital to appreciate that *we are as sick as our secrets.*

There are certain forms of stress which we all tend to keep well hidden. We conceal or suppress what is troubling us, foolishly thinking that somehow we are controlling it by doing so. But the harder we try to hold on to it, the tighter will be its grip on us.

The ability to let go is a powerful weapon in the fight against stress. It's a release which allows our spirit to heal. It is a great help, therefore, to find a way of expressing what you are feeling. You can talk with a friend, or write a poem, or paint a picture of it. You can scream and shout, or cry your heart out. You can give expression to it in dreams or in hard work.

How you do it doesn't matter. The important thing is to bring it out into the light. Then you can clarify it, get it into some sort of perspective, and cut it down to size. If you cannot *name* it, you can't *claim* it and you certainly cannot even begin to *tame* it.

LOVE ALL THREE

The secret of every successful stress management programme is that it is essentially a lifestyle programme, not a quick fix or attempt at problem-solving. This final step of learning to love our self, our enemy and our friends is vital. We can tolerate a great deal of what we now consider to be intolerable stress, if we learn the core of this message.

If we do not love ourselves, our motivation for getting rid of our stress may not be strong enough for us to take the sometimes difficult decisions required. Without this step we will not believe in our ability to cope or trust the skills we already have. Without a healthy self-love we will be prone to reject the dark side of ourselves. In doing so, we may never understand or experience what Carl Jung spoke about when he said that our shadow can be 90% gold.

If we do not learn to love our enemy, we will not make the effort to get to know more about it. This means we won't know exactly what we are dealing with. We'll consistently minimize the often tragic effects of stress and not take them seriously. Consequently, we will see no need to take the steps needed to prevent stress, no matter how simple or obvious.

If we do not learn to love our friends, we may be too quick to dismiss them as being ineffective, without ever really having given them a chance to work. We will tend to value the new at the expense of the old. We will be prepared to try out difficult and complicated techniques, while at the same time putting down the old tried-and-true remedies of the past. When it comes to stress and the harm it can do, we need to be humble enough the value *all* our friends, no matter how silly or far-fetched we think they are.

The wisdom of the tortoise is well worth learning. As is the beautiful 'serenity prayer' of Reinhold Niebuhr:

> *God, grant me*
> *the serenity to accept the things I cannot change;*
> *courage to change the things I can;*
> *and the wisdom to know the difference.*